W9-BRB-215

Address & Telephone Book

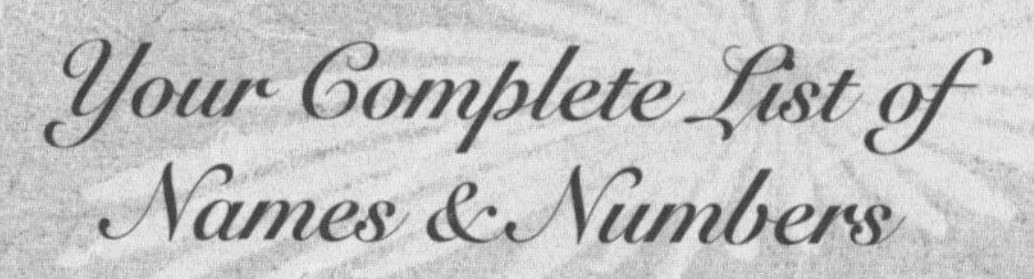

Your Complete List of Names & Numbers

A

NAME TELEPHONE

ADDRESS

FAX

NAME TELEPHONE

ADDRESS

FAX

NAME TELEPHONE

ADDRESS

FAX

NAME TELEPHONE

ADDRESS

FAX

NAME TELEPHONE

ADDRESS

FAX

NAME TELEPHONE

ADDRESS

FAX

NAME TELEPHONE

ADDRESS

FAX

NAME TELEPHONE

ADDRESS

FAX

NAME TELEPHONE

ADDRESS

FAX

NAME TELEPHONE

ADDRESS

FAX

NAME TELEPHONE

ADDRESS

FAX

NAME TELEPHONE

ADDRESS

FAX

NAME TELEPHONE

ADDRESS

FAX

NAME TELEPHONE

ADDRESS

FAX

NAME TELEPHONE

ADDRESS

FAX

NAME TELEPHONE

ADDRESS

FAX

NAME TELEPHONE

ADDRESS

FAX

NAME TELEPHONE

ADDRESS

FAX

NAME TELEPHONE

ADDRESS

FAX

NAME TELEPHONE

ADDRESS

FAX

B

NAME TELEPHONE

ADDRESS

FAX

NAME TELEPHONE

ADDRESS

FAX

NAME TELEPHONE

ADDRESS

FAX

NAME TELEPHONE

ADDRESS

FAX

NAME TELEPHONE

ADDRESS

FAX

NAME TELEPHONE

ADDRESS

FAX

NAME TELEPHONE

ADDRESS

FAX

NAME TELEPHONE

ADDRESS

FAX

NAME TELEPHONE

ADDRESS

FAX

NAME TELEPHONE

ADDRESS

FAX

NAME TELEPHONE

ADDRESS

FAX

NAME TELEPHONE

ADDRESS

FAX

NAME TELEPHONE

ADDRESS

FAX

NAME TELEPHONE

ADDRESS

FAX

NAME TELEPHONE

ADDRESS

FAX

NAME TELEPHONE

ADDRESS

FAX

NAME TELEPHONE

ADDRESS

FAX

NAME TELEPHONE

ADDRESS

FAX

NAME TELEPHONE

ADDRESS

FAX

NAME TELEPHONE

ADDRESS

FAX

6

NAME TELEPHONE

ADDRESS

FAX

NAME TELEPHONE

ADDRESS

FAX

NAME TELEPHONE

ADDRESS

FAX

NAME TELEPHONE

ADDRESS

FAX

NAME TELEPHONE

ADDRESS

FAX

NAME TELEPHONE

ADDRESS

FAX

NAME TELEPHONE

ADDRESS

FAX

NAME TELEPHONE

ADDRESS

FAX

NAME TELEPHONE

ADDRESS

FAX

NAME TELEPHONE

ADDRESS

FAX

NAME TELEPHONE

ADDRESS

FAX

NAME TELEPHONE

ADDRESS

FAX

NAME TELEPHONE

ADDRESS

FAX

NAME TELEPHONE

ADDRESS

FAX

NAME TELEPHONE

ADDRESS

FAX

NAME TELEPHONE

ADDRESS

FAX

NAME TELEPHONE

ADDRESS

FAX

NAME TELEPHONE

ADDRESS

FAX

NAME TELEPHONE

ADDRESS

FAX

NAME TELEPHONE

ADDRESS

FAX

D

NAME | TELEPHONE
ADDRESS
FAX

NAME | TELEPHONE
ADDRESS
FAX

NAME | TELEPHONE
ADDRESS
FAX

NAME | TELEPHONE
ADDRESS
FAX

NAME | TELEPHONE
ADDRESS
FAX

NAME

TELEPHONE

ADDRESS

FAX

NAME

TELEPHONE

ADDRESS

FAX

NAME

TELEPHONE

ADDRESS

FAX

NAME

TELEPHONE

ADDRESS

FAX

NAME

TELEPHONE

ADDRESS

FAX

NAME TELEPHONE

ADDRESS

FAX

NAME TELEPHONE

ADDRESS

FAX

NAME TELEPHONE

ADDRESS

FAX

NAME TELEPHONE

ADDRESS

FAX

NAME TELEPHONE

ADDRESS

FAX

NAME TELEPHONE

ADDRESS

FAX

NAME TELEPHONE

ADDRESS

FAX

NAME TELEPHONE

ADDRESS

FAX

NAME TELEPHONE

ADDRESS

FAX

NAME TELEPHONE

ADDRESS

FAX

E

NAME TELEPHONE

ADDRESS

FAX

NAME TELEPHONE

ADDRESS

FAX

NAME TELEPHONE

ADDRESS

FAX

NAME TELEPHONE

ADDRESS

FAX

NAME TELEPHONE

ADDRESS

FAX

NAME TELEPHONE

ADDRESS

FAX

NAME TELEPHONE

ADDRESS

FAX

NAME TELEPHONE

ADDRESS

FAX

NAME TELEPHONE

ADDRESS

FAX

NAME TELEPHONE

ADDRESS

FAX

NAME *TELEPHONE*

ADDRESS

FAX

NAME *TELEPHONE*

ADDRESS

FAX

NAME *TELEPHONE*

ADDRESS

FAX

NAME *TELEPHONE*

ADDRESS

FAX

NAME *TELEPHONE*

ADDRESS

FAX

NAME TELEPHONE

ADDRESS

FAX

NAME TELEPHONE

ADDRESS

FAX

NAME TELEPHONE

ADDRESS

FAX

NAME TELEPHONE

ADDRESS

FAX

NAME TELEPHONE

ADDRESS

FAX

F

NAME TELEPHONE

ADDRESS

FAX

NAME TELEPHONE

ADDRESS

FAX

NAME TELEPHONE

ADDRESS

FAX

NAME TELEPHONE

ADDRESS

FAX

NAME TELEPHONE

ADDRESS

FAX

NAME
TELEPHONE
ADDRESS
FAX

NAME
TELEPHONE
ADDRESS
FAX

NAME
TELEPHONE
ADDRESS
FAX

NAME
TELEPHONE
ADDRESS
FAX

NAME
TELEPHONE
ADDRESS
FAX

NAME TELEPHONE

ADDRESS

FAX

NAME TELEPHONE

ADDRESS

FAX

NAME TELEPHONE

ADDRESS

FAX

NAME TELEPHONE

ADDRESS

FAX

NAME TELEPHONE

ADDRESS

FAX

NAME TELEPHONE

ADDRESS

FAX

NAME TELEPHONE

ADDRESS

FAX

NAME TELEPHONE

ADDRESS

FAX

NAME TELEPHONE

ADDRESS

FAX

NAME TELEPHONE

ADDRESS

FAX

G

NAME TELEPHONE

ADDRESS

FAX

NAME TELEPHONE

ADDRESS

FAX

NAME TELEPHONE

ADDRESS

FAX

NAME TELEPHONE

ADDRESS

FAX

NAME TELEPHONE

ADDRESS

FAX

Name
Telephone
Address
Fax

Name
Telephone
Address
Fax

Name
Telephone
Address
Fax

Name
Telephone
Address
Fax

Name
Telephone
Address
Fax

NAME TELEPHONE

ADDRESS

FAX

NAME TELEPHONE

ADDRESS

FAX

NAME TELEPHONE

ADDRESS

FAX

NAME TELEPHONE

ADDRESS

FAX

NAME TELEPHONE

ADDRESS

FAX

NAME TELEPHONE

ADDRESS

FAX

NAME TELEPHONE

ADDRESS

FAX

NAME TELEPHONE

ADDRESS

FAX

NAME TELEPHONE

ADDRESS

FAX

NAME TELEPHONE

ADDRESS

FAX

H

NAME TELEPHONE

ADDRESS

FAX

NAME TELEPHONE

ADDRESS

FAX

NAME TELEPHONE

ADDRESS

FAX

NAME TELEPHONE

ADDRESS

FAX

NAME TELEPHONE

ADDRESS

FAX

NAME TELEPHONE
ADDRESS
FAX

NAME TELEPHONE
ADDRESS
FAX

NAME TELEPHONE
ADDRESS
FAX

NAME TELEPHONE
ADDRESS
FAX

NAME TELEPHONE
ADDRESS
FAX

NAME TELEPHONE

ADDRESS

FAX

NAME TELEPHONE

ADDRESS

FAX

NAME TELEPHONE

ADDRESS

FAX

NAME TELEPHONE

ADDRESS

FAX

NAME TELEPHONE

ADDRESS

FAX

NAME TELEPHONE

ADDRESS

FAX

NAME TELEPHONE

ADDRESS

FAX

NAME TELEPHONE

ADDRESS

FAX

NAME TELEPHONE

ADDRESS

FAX

NAME TELEPHONE

ADDRESS

FAX

T

NAME TELEPHONE

ADDRESS

FAX

NAME TELEPHONE

ADDRESS

FAX

NAME TELEPHONE

ADDRESS

FAX

NAME TELEPHONE

ADDRESS

FAX

NAME TELEPHONE

ADDRESS

FAX

NAME TELEPHONE

ADDRESS

FAX

NAME TELEPHONE

ADDRESS

FAX

NAME TELEPHONE

ADDRESS

FAX

NAME TELEPHONE

ADDRESS

FAX

NAME TELEPHONE

ADDRESS

FAX

NAME TELEPHONE

ADDRESS

FAX

NAME TELEPHONE

ADDRESS

FAX

NAME TELEPHONE

ADDRESS

FAX

NAME TELEPHONE

ADDRESS

FAX

NAME TELEPHONE

ADDRESS

FAX

NAME TELEPHONE

ADDRESS

FAX

NAME TELEPHONE

ADDRESS

FAX

NAME TELEPHONE

ADDRESS

FAX

NAME TELEPHONE

ADDRESS

FAX

NAME TELEPHONE

ADDRESS

FAX

J

NAME *TELEPHONE*

ADDRESS

FAX

NAME *TELEPHONE*

ADDRESS

FAX

NAME *TELEPHONE*

ADDRESS

FAX

NAME *TELEPHONE*

ADDRESS

FAX

NAME *TELEPHONE*

ADDRESS

FAX

NAME TELEPHONE

ADDRESS

FAX

NAME TELEPHONE

ADDRESS

FAX

NAME TELEPHONE

ADDRESS

FAX

NAME TELEPHONE

ADDRESS

FAX

NAME TELEPHONE

ADDRESS

FAX

Name *Telephone*

Address

Fax

Name *Telephone*

Address

Fax

Name *Telephone*

Address

Fax

Name *Telephone*

Address

Fax

Name *Telephone*

Address

Fax

NAME TELEPHONE

ADDRESS

FAX

NAME TELEPHONE

ADDRESS

FAX

NAME TELEPHONE

ADDRESS

FAX

NAME TELEPHONE

ADDRESS

FAX

NAME TELEPHONE

ADDRESS

FAX

K

NAME TELEPHONE

ADDRESS

FAX

NAME TELEPHONE

ADDRESS

FAX

NAME TELEPHONE

ADDRESS

FAX

NAME TELEPHONE

ADDRESS

FAX

NAME TELEPHONE

ADDRESS

FAX

NAME TELEPHONE

ADDRESS

FAX

NAME TELEPHONE

ADDRESS

FAX

NAME TELEPHONE

ADDRESS

FAX

NAME TELEPHONE

ADDRESS

FAX

NAME TELEPHONE

ADDRESS

FAX

NAME TELEPHONE

ADDRESS

FAX

NAME TELEPHONE

ADDRESS

FAX

NAME TELEPHONE

ADDRESS

FAX

NAME TELEPHONE

ADDRESS

FAX

NAME TELEPHONE

ADDRESS

FAX

NAME TELEPHONE

ADDRESS

FAX

NAME TELEPHONE

ADDRESS

FAX

NAME TELEPHONE

ADDRESS

FAX

NAME TELEPHONE

ADDRESS

FAX

NAME TELEPHONE

ADDRESS

FAX

L

NAME TELEPHONE
ADDRESS
FAX

NAME TELEPHONE
ADDRESS
FAX

NAME TELEPHONE
ADDRESS
FAX

NAME TELEPHONE
ADDRESS
FAX

NAME TELEPHONE
ADDRESS
FAX

NAME *TELEPHONE*

ADDRESS

FAX

NAME *TELEPHONE*

ADDRESS

FAX

L

NAME *TELEPHONE*

ADDRESS

FAX

NAME *TELEPHONE*

ADDRESS

FAX

NAME *TELEPHONE*

ADDRESS

FAX

NAME TELEPHONE

ADDRESS

FAX

NAME TELEPHONE

ADDRESS

FAX

NAME TELEPHONE

ADDRESS

FAX

NAME TELEPHONE

ADDRESS

FAX

NAME TELEPHONE

ADDRESS

FAX

NAME TELEPHONE

ADDRESS

FAX

NAME TELEPHONE

ADDRESS

FAX

NAME TELEPHONE

ADDRESS

FAX

NAME TELEPHONE

ADDRESS

FAX

NAME TELEPHONE

ADDRESS

FAX

M

NAME TELEPHONE

ADDRESS

FAX

NAME TELEPHONE

ADDRESS

FAX

NAME TELEPHONE

ADDRESS

FAX

NAME TELEPHONE

ADDRESS

FAX

NAME TELEPHONE

ADDRESS

FAX

NAME TELEPHONE

ADDRESS

FAX

NAME TELEPHONE

ADDRESS

FAX

NAME TELEPHONE

ADDRESS

FAX

NAME TELEPHONE

ADDRESS

FAX

NAME TELEPHONE

ADDRESS

FAX

NAME TELEPHONE

ADDRESS

FAX

NAME TELEPHONE

ADDRESS

FAX

NAME TELEPHONE

ADDRESS

FAX

NAME TELEPHONE

ADDRESS

FAX

NAME TELEPHONE

ADDRESS

FAX

NAME TELEPHONE

ADDRESS

FAX

NAME TELEPHONE

ADDRESS

FAX

NAME TELEPHONE

ADDRESS

FAX

NAME TELEPHONE

ADDRESS

FAX

NAME TELEPHONE

ADDRESS

FAX

N

NAME TELEPHONE

ADDRESS

FAX

NAME TELEPHONE

ADDRESS

FAX

NAME TELEPHONE

ADDRESS

FAX

NAME TELEPHONE

ADDRESS

FAX

NAME TELEPHONE

ADDRESS

FAX

NAME TELEPHONE

ADDRESS

FAX

NAME TELEPHONE

ADDRESS

FAX

NAME TELEPHONE

ADDRESS

FAX

NAME TELEPHONE

ADDRESS

FAX

NAME TELEPHONE

ADDRESS

FAX

NAME TELEPHONE
ADDRESS
FAX

NAME TELEPHONE
ADDRESS
FAX

NAME TELEPHONE
ADDRESS
FAX

NAME TELEPHONE
ADDRESS
FAX

NAME TELEPHONE
ADDRESS
FAX

NAME TELEPHONE

ADDRESS

FAX

NAME TELEPHONE

ADDRESS

FAX

NAME TELEPHONE

ADDRESS

FAX

NAME TELEPHONE

ADDRESS

FAX

NAME TELEPHONE

ADDRESS

FAX

O

NAME TELEPHONE

ADDRESS

FAX

NAME TELEPHONE

ADDRESS

FAX

NAME TELEPHONE

ADDRESS

FAX

NAME TELEPHONE

ADDRESS

FAX

NAME TELEPHONE

ADDRESS

FAX

NAME TELEPHONE

ADDRESS

FAX

NAME TELEPHONE

ADDRESS

FAX

NAME TELEPHONE

ADDRESS

FAX

NAME TELEPHONE

ADDRESS

FAX

NAME TELEPHONE

ADDRESS

FAX

NAME TELEPHONE

ADDRESS

FAX

NAME TELEPHONE

ADDRESS

FAX

NAME TELEPHONE

ADDRESS

FAX

NAME TELEPHONE

ADDRESS

FAX

NAME TELEPHONE

ADDRESS

FAX

NAME | TELEPHONE
ADDRESS
FAX

NAME | TELEPHONE
ADDRESS
FAX

NAME | TELEPHONE
ADDRESS
FAX

NAME | TELEPHONE
ADDRESS
FAX

NAME | TELEPHONE
ADDRESS
FAX

P

NAME TELEPHONE

ADDRESS

FAX

NAME TELEPHONE

ADDRESS

FAX

NAME TELEPHONE

ADDRESS

FAX

NAME TELEPHONE

ADDRESS

FAX

NAME TELEPHONE

ADDRESS

FAX

NAME TELEPHONE

ADDRESS

FAX

NAME TELEPHONE

ADDRESS

FAX

NAME TELEPHONE

ADDRESS

FAX

P

NAME TELEPHONE

ADDRESS

FAX

NAME TELEPHONE

ADDRESS

FAX

NAME TELEPHONE

ADDRESS

FAX

NAME TELEPHONE

ADDRESS

FAX

NAME TELEPHONE

ADDRESS

FAX

NAME TELEPHONE

ADDRESS

FAX

NAME TELEPHONE

ADDRESS

FAX

NAME TELEPHONE

ADDRESS

FAX

NAME TELEPHONE

ADDRESS

FAX

NAME TELEPHONE

ADDRESS

FAX

NAME TELEPHONE

ADDRESS

FAX

NAME TELEPHONE

ADDRESS

FAX

2

NAME TELEPHONE

ADDRESS

FAX

NAME TELEPHONE

ADDRESS

FAX

NAME TELEPHONE

ADDRESS

FAX

NAME TELEPHONE

ADDRESS

FAX

NAME TELEPHONE

ADDRESS

FAX

NAME TELEPHONE
ADDRESS
FAX

NAME TELEPHONE
ADDRESS
FAX

NAME TELEPHONE
ADDRESS
FAX

NAME TELEPHONE
ADDRESS
FAX

NAME TELEPHONE
ADDRESS
FAX

NAME TELEPHONE

ADDRESS

FAX

NAME TELEPHONE

ADDRESS

FAX

NAME TELEPHONE

ADDRESS

FAX

NAME TELEPHONE

ADDRESS

FAX

NAME TELEPHONE

ADDRESS

FAX

NAME TELEPHONE

ADDRESS

FAX

NAME TELEPHONE

ADDRESS

FAX

NAME TELEPHONE

ADDRESS

FAX

NAME TELEPHONE

ADDRESS

FAX

NAME TELEPHONE

ADDRESS

FAX

R

NAME TELEPHONE

ADDRESS

FAX

NAME TELEPHONE

ADDRESS

FAX

NAME TELEPHONE

ADDRESS

FAX

NAME TELEPHONE

ADDRESS

FAX

NAME TELEPHONE

ADDRESS

FAX

NAME TELEPHONE

ADDRESS

FAX

NAME TELEPHONE

ADDRESS

FAX

NAME TELEPHONE

ADDRESS

FAX

NAME TELEPHONE

ADDRESS

FAX

NAME TELEPHONE

ADDRESS

FAX

NAME TELEPHONE

ADDRESS

FAX

NAME TELEPHONE

ADDRESS

FAX

NAME TELEPHONE

ADDRESS

FAX

NAME TELEPHONE

ADDRESS

FAX

NAME TELEPHONE

ADDRESS

FAX

NAME TELEPHONE

ADDRESS

FAX

NAME TELEPHONE

ADDRESS

FAX

NAME TELEPHONE

ADDRESS

FAX

NAME TELEPHONE

ADDRESS

FAX

NAME TELEPHONE

ADDRESS

FAX

S

NAME TELEPHONE

ADDRESS

FAX

NAME TELEPHONE

ADDRESS

FAX

NAME TELEPHONE

ADDRESS

FAX

NAME TELEPHONE

ADDRESS

FAX

NAME TELEPHONE

ADDRESS

FAX

NAME TELEPHONE

ADDRESS

FAX

NAME TELEPHONE

ADDRESS

FAX

NAME TELEPHONE

ADDRESS

FAX

NAME TELEPHONE

ADDRESS

FAX

S

NAME TELEPHONE

ADDRESS

FAX

NAME TELEPHONE

ADDRESS

FAX

NAME TELEPHONE

ADDRESS

FAX

NAME TELEPHONE

ADDRESS

FAX

NAME TELEPHONE

ADDRESS

FAX

NAME TELEPHONE

ADDRESS

FAX

NAME TELEPHONE

ADDRESS

FAX

NAME TELEPHONE

ADDRESS

FAX

NAME TELEPHONE

ADDRESS

FAX

NAME TELEPHONE

ADDRESS

FAX

NAME TELEPHONE

ADDRESS

FAX

T

NAME TELEPHONE

ADDRESS

FAX

NAME TELEPHONE

ADDRESS

FAX

NAME TELEPHONE

ADDRESS

FAX

NAME TELEPHONE

ADDRESS

FAX

NAME TELEPHONE

ADDRESS

FAX

NAME TELEPHONE

ADDRESS

FAX

NAME TELEPHONE

ADDRESS

FAX

NAME TELEPHONE

ADDRESS

FAX

NAME TELEPHONE

ADDRESS

FAX

T

NAME TELEPHONE

ADDRESS

FAX

NAME TELEPHONE

ADDRESS

FAX

NAME TELEPHONE

ADDRESS

FAX

NAME TELEPHONE

ADDRESS

FAX

NAME TELEPHONE

ADDRESS

FAX

NAME TELEPHONE

ADDRESS

FAX

T

NAME TELEPHONE

ADDRESS

FAX

NAME TELEPHONE

ADDRESS

FAX

NAME TELEPHONE

ADDRESS

FAX

NAME TELEPHONE

ADDRESS

FAX

NAME TELEPHONE

ADDRESS

FAX

UV

NAME TELEPHONE

ADDRESS

FAX

NAME TELEPHONE

ADDRESS

FAX

NAME TELEPHONE

ADDRESS

FAX

NAME TELEPHONE

ADDRESS

FAX

NAME TELEPHONE

ADDRESS

FAX

NAME TELEPHONE

ADDRESS

FAX

NAME TELEPHONE

ADDRESS

FAX

NAME TELEPHONE

ADDRESS

FAX

NAME TELEPHONE

ADDRESS

FAX

NAME TELEPHONE

ADDRESS

FAX

NAME TELEPHONE

ADDRESS

FAX

NAME TELEPHONE

ADDRESS

FAX

NAME TELEPHONE

ADDRESS

FAX

NAME TELEPHONE

ADDRESS

FAX

NAME TELEPHONE

ADDRESS

FAX

NAME TELEPHONE

ADDRESS

FAX

NAME TELEPHONE

ADDRESS

FAX

NAME TELEPHONE

ADDRESS

FAX

NAME TELEPHONE

ADDRESS

FAX

NAME TELEPHONE

ADDRESS

FAX

W

NAME TELEPHONE

ADDRESS

FAX

NAME TELEPHONE

ADDRESS

FAX

NAME TELEPHONE

ADDRESS

FAX

NAME TELEPHONE

ADDRESS

FAX

NAME TELEPHONE

ADDRESS

FAX

Name *Telephone*

Address

Fax

Name *Telephone*

Address

Fax

Name *Telephone*

Address

Fax

Name *Telephone*

Address

Fax

Name *Telephone*

Address

Fax

NAME TELEPHONE
ADDRESS
FAX

NAME TELEPHONE
ADDRESS
FAX

NAME TELEPHONE
ADDRESS
FAX

NAME TELEPHONE
ADDRESS
FAX

NAME TELEPHONE
ADDRESS
FAX

NAME TELEPHONE

ADDRESS

FAX

NAME TELEPHONE

ADDRESS

FAX

NAME TELEPHONE

ADDRESS

FAX

NAME TELEPHONE

ADDRESS

FAX

NAME TELEPHONE

ADDRESS

FAX

XY

NAME TELEPHONE

ADDRESS

FAX

NAME TELEPHONE

ADDRESS

FAX

NAME TELEPHONE

ADDRESS

FAX

NAME TELEPHONE

ADDRESS

FAX

NAME TELEPHONE

ADDRESS

FAX

NAME TELEPHONE

ADDRESS

FAX

NAME TELEPHONE

ADDRESS

FAX

NAME TELEPHONE

ADDRESS

FAX

NAME TELEPHONE

ADDRESS

FAX

NAME TELEPHONE

ADDRESS

FAX

NAME TELEPHONE

ADDRESS

FAX

NAME TELEPHONE

ADDRESS

FAX

NAME TELEPHONE

ADDRESS

FAX

NAME TELEPHONE

ADDRESS

FAX

NAME TELEPHONE

ADDRESS

FAX

NAME TELEPHONE

ADDRESS

FAX

NAME TELEPHONE

ADDRESS

FAX

NAME TELEPHONE

ADDRESS

FAX

NAME TELEPHONE

ADDRESS

FAX

NAME TELEPHONE

ADDRESS

FAX

Z